4

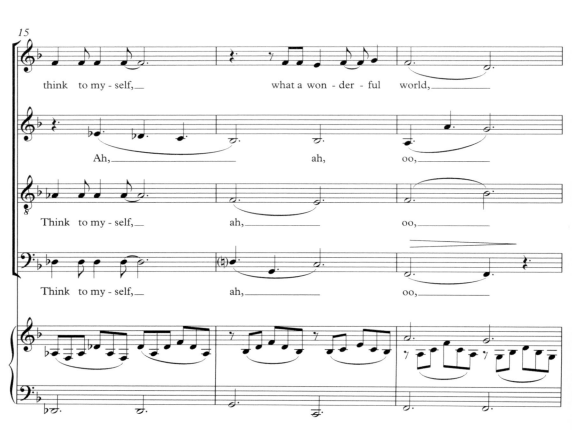

6

Novello Publishing Limited
part of The Music Sales Group
14-15 Berners Street
London W1T 3LJ, UK
www.chesternovello.com

This publication © 2009 Novello & Company Limited

Exclusive distributors:
Hal Leonard Europe Limited
Newmarket Road, Bury St Edmunds
Suffolk IP33 3YB

ISBN 978-1-84938-115-4

EXCLUSIVELY DISTRIBUTED BY
HAL•LEONARD®

9 781849 381154